★ COMICS BY ★

JENNIFER L. HOLM & MATTHEW HOLM
JARRETT J. KROSOCZKA
DAV PILKEY
DAN SANTAT
RAINA TELGEMEIER & DAVE ROMAN
URSULA VERNON
ERIC WIGHT
GENE LUEN YANG

COMICS SQUAD
RECESS!

· EDITED BY ·

JENNIFER L. HOLM, MATTHEW HOLM &
JARRETT J. KROSOCZKA

Better than
Pizza Day!

TA-DA!

SCHOLASTIC INC.

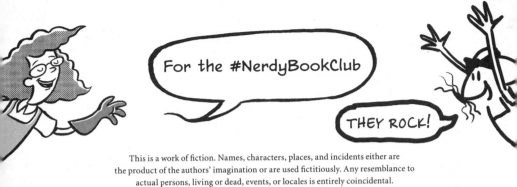

For the #NerdyBookClub

THEY ROCK!

ISBN 978-1-338-04830-8

12 11 10 9 8 7 6 5 4 3 2 1   16 17 18 19 20 21

Printed in the U.S.A.   23

First Scholastic printing, April 2016

★ CONTENTS ★

I just want to smother these stories in gravy and eat them up!

THE SUPER-SECRET NINJA CLUB
BY GENE LUEN YANG . . . 1

BOOK 'EM, DOG MAN!
BY DAV PILKEY . . . 17

BETTY AND THE PERILOUS PIZZA DAY
BY JARRETT J. KROSOCZKA . . . 37

THE MAGIC ACORN
BY URSULA VERNON . . . 55

BABYMOUSE: THE QUEST FOR RECESS
BY JENNIFER L. HOLM & MATTHEW HOLM . . . 71

JIMINY SPRINKLES IN "FREEZE TAG"
BY ERIC WIGHT . . . 89

300 WORDS
BY DAN SANTAT . . . 103

THE RAINY DAY MONITOR
BY RAINA TELGEMEIER & DAVE ROMAN . . . 119

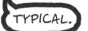

THEY TOLD ME I'D BE FIRST!

TYPICAL.

THE SUPER-SECRET NINJA CLUB

by
Gene Luen Yang

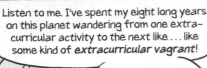

Listen to me. I've spent my eight long years on this planet wandering from one extra-curricular activity to the next like . . . like some kind of *extracurricular vagrant*!

I've tried piano, tee ball, roller skating, finger painting . . . none of them fit me. I got so desperate, I even asked my folks to sign me up for a pipe cleaner sculpture class last summer!

Think about that, guys! I spent *six weeks* making little animals out of fuzzy, colored wire!

Yikes.

Not once did I ever feel at *peace*. Not once did I ever feel at *home*.

But now, in this place, at this moment... I discover *you*, my fellow classmates, gathered in a circle of *brotherhood*, wearing masks of *honor*, your hearts burning for *justice*!

Is your heart burning?

Kinda, but I just ate like twenty Tater Tots.

Finally, my *DESTINY* has descended upon me like a revelation from the heavens! I was born to be a member of the *Super-Secret Ninja Club*!

BRiiNG!

Aw, man! Lunch is over and we wasted our entire meeting listening to Daryl make a stupid speech! And he's not even a *ninja*!

You mean, not a ninja *yet*!

No, we mean not a ninja *ever*!

What?! You guys can't do this to me! You can't deny a person his *destiny*!

Oh, just watch me! I'm about to deny you right in the forehead!

Stop, *stop*! You guys go to class! I'll handle this!

Go!

Discipline #1:
Seishinteki kyōyō
Spiritual Refinement

Daryl! Get off the coffee table!

Discipline #2:
Taijutsu
Unarmed Combat

Tap out! TAP OUT!

Discipline #3:
Kenjutsu
Sword Techniques

Discipline #4:
Bōjutsu
Staff Techniques

Discipline #5:
Sōjutsu
Spear Techniques

Discipline #6:
Naginatajutsu
Pole Weapon Techniques

Discipline #7:
Shinobi-iri
Entering Techniques

Discipline #8:
Intonjutsu
Escaping Techniques

Discipline #9:
Kusarigamajutsu
Chain Weapon
Techniques

Anyone seen the snowflake chain that's supposed to go around the Christmas tree?

HIIII-YAH!

Discipline #10:
Shurikenjutsu
Throwing Weapons
Techniques

Anyone seen the star that's supposed to go on top of the Christmas tree?

HIIII-YAH!

Discipline #11:
Kayakujutsu
Pyrotechnics

Anyone seen the lights that are supposed to be on the outside of the house?

HIIII-YAH!

Discipline #12:
Hensōjutsu
Impersonation

Are *you* the true Santa... or am *I*?

?

Discipline #13:
Bajutsu
Horsemanship

HIIII-YAH!

Discipline #14:
Sui-ren
Water Training

HIIII-YAH!

?

10

Discipline #15:
Tenmon
Meteorology

Discipline #16:
Chi-mon
Geography

Discipline #17:
Bōryaku
Political Tactics

Discipline #18:
Chōhō
Espionage

I hope you had a good Winter Recess, my ninja brothers!

AAH!

Don't be scared! It's me, Daryl!

Oh, hey, Daryl. Why do you have an ugly sweater wrapped around your head?

Sigh. I asked for a black T-shirt, but Auntie Lulu got me this instead.

But listen, guys! I did it! It took me two weeks, but *I did it!*

You did what?

I developed **super-awesome ninja skills**! I've become a **super-awesome ninja**! I'm finally ready to join the *SUPER-SECRET NINJA CLUB!*

What are you talking about?

bounce!

POP!

FFFFFFWOOOSH....

Dodgeball is NOT super-awesome!

FFFWTT... flop!

Whoa.

Daryl kind of owes me a new ball, but I'm too afraid to ask.

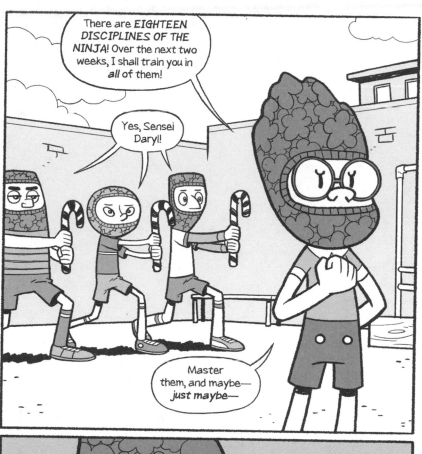

There are *EIGHTEEN DISCIPLINES OF THE NINJA*! Over the next two weeks, I shall train you in *all* of them!

Yes, Sensei Daryl!

Master them, and maybe— *just maybe*—

—you'll be as SUPER-AWESOME as ME!

END.

MASH-UP MADNESS!

BABYMOUSE   LUNCH LADY   LUNCH MOUSE

BETTY   SQUISH   SQUISHETTY

LOCKER   FLIPPY BUNNY   FLIPPY LOCKER

NOW GO TRY DRAWING YOUR OWN MASH-UPS!

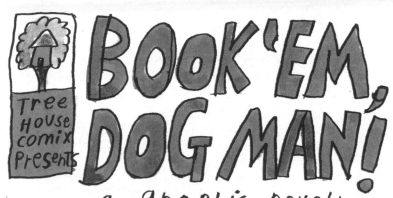

BOOK'EM, DOG MAN!

Tree House comix Presents

a graphic novella

Akshin

LaFFs

FLip-O-rama

BY George B. and Harold H.

Jerome Horwitz Elementary School

We put the "ow" in Knowledge

Dear Mr. and Mrs. Beard,

Once again I am writing to inform you of your son's disruptive activity in my classroom.

The assignment was to create a WRITTEN public service message to promote reading. Your son and his friend Harold Hutchins (I am sending a nearly identical letter to Harold's mother) were specifically told NOT to make a comic book for this assignment.

As usual, they did exactly what they were told *not* to do (see attached comic book). When I confronted George about his disobedience, he claimed that this was not a comic book, but a "graphic novella." I am getting fed up with George's impudence.

I have told both boys on numerous occasions that the classroom is no place for creativity, yet they continue to make these obnoxious and offensive "comix." As you will see, this comic book contains multiple scenes of stealing, violence, and unlawfulness . . . and don't get me started on the spelling and grammar!

George's silly, disruptive behavior, as well as these increasingly disturbing comic books, are turning my classroom into a zoo. I have spoken to Principal Krupp about *Dog Man* on numerous occasions. We both believe that you should consider psychological counseling for your son, or at the very least some kind of behavior modification drug to cure him of his "creative streak."

Regretfully,

Ms. Construde

Ms. Construde
Grade 1 Teacher

BOOK 'EM, DOG MAN

Tree House Comix

BY George B. and Harold H.

One day Petey sat in his jail cell feeling sad.

News DOG man wins again

Rats! Every time I have a evil plan, DOG man always OUT-smarts me!

How come Hes so Darn smart???

So Petey De-siDid to find out!

That Day in the Jailyard, Petey Got a exscape plan.

He sat on the see saw...

Yo! Big Jim! come over and see saw with me!!!

ok!

weee

bonk

CAT JAIL

So Long, suckas!

I'm Free!

Now to find out what makes DOG man so smart!

So Petey sneaked to DOG mans House.

hmm... Hes reading!

21

Before too long...

Rats! all the books on earth are blank!

aw man!

woe is us!

Soon every body forgotted about reading

OH well

what ever

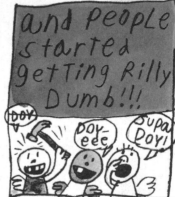

and people started getting rilly dumb!!!

DOY

DOY-eee

Supa Doy!

2 weeks later.

Awesome!

Petey's secrit lab

DUMB   OK   smart   Jean Yiss   Supa Dumb

The world is supa dumb!!!

nows my chanse to have some fun...

Petey walked to the fansy car lot.

Hey, bub!!! Gimme a car!

Duh, my cat had eleven-teen puppies.

Okaaaaay...

I'm just gonna take that one over there!

Duh, my mommy is five years old.

And so... That was easy!!!

THEN

Yee Haw!

DOG man smelled a cat.

and his "DOG instinkts" took over.

DOG Man FolLOWeD The Cat smeLL to Peteys hideout.

Peteys secrit Lab

he went inside...

...and found Peteys secrit stash OF Books.

DOG man started to read...

DOG man Read all nite Long...

...and GOT smarter and smarter.

The next morning, DOG man had a plan.

PETEYS secrit LaB

He Brought PETEYS BOOKS to The SCHooL.

SCHooL

and GaVeD Them TO The Kids.

Read, darn ya, Read!!

Soon, Petey woked up...

...to a shock!

MY BOOKS!

Petey followed the trail of books.

Pete secr lab

It leaded to the school.

School

Then the
Resess Bell
~m~~ Rang!

OOL

SCHOOL

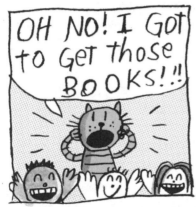

OH NO! I Got
to Get those
BOOKS!!!

TRiPLe FLiP-O-RAMAS

animate the action cheesily. Heres How:

Hold Book
open Like
this.

Flip Page
33 Back
and Forth.

add your
own sound
afecks!

Left
Hand Here

The Swing Set Smacker

The See Saw Smoosher

Spring Break

RIGHT THUM HERE

33

The
Swing
Set
Smacker

The
see
saw
Smoosher

Spring
Break

So Petey got capchered...

Rats!

... Dog Man reversed the Word-B-Gone 2000

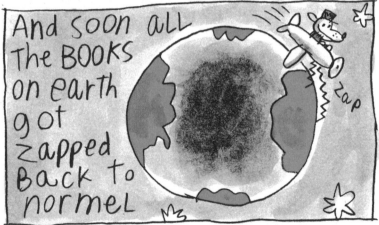

And soon all the books on earth got zapped back to normel

zap

Horay for Dog Man!!!

Betty

and the
Perilous Pizza Day

I think I
have it. . . .

a LUNCH LADY mini-comic

Jarrett J. Krosoczka

Oatmeal Blaster

Hmph! Well, so much for that!

Betty! Come in, Betty!

Mole Communicator

Lunch Lady, this is Betty, over!

cough cough Betty, how did breakfast go?

I'd say it was a big hit! Can't go wrong with waffle tacos!

cough cough Betty, I just can't shake this cold. I'm not going to be able to make it in to work today after all. *cough cough*

But today is . . .

PIZZA DAY!

I'm so sorry, Betty. But you're going to have to cover lunch all by yourself.

Roger that, Lunch Lady.

Hundreds of hungry kids on their favorite lunch day of the week!

I'll never make all the pizzas in time!

Unless . . .

FLOOP

Perfect! Now just a few dozen more and . . .

DING! DANG! DOONG! DOOP!

Jumping jelly beans!

47

The Pizza Monster! I can't let it attack the school's head honcho! My cover will be blown! Ugh! What would Lunch Lady do?!

Principal Hernandez, we have a situation here in the boys' room. Need backup ASAP!

Please don't tell me it's Milmoe again. I'll be right there!

Come on out and play, buddy!

CLANK!

WHOOP!

RECESS IS
OVER IN TEN MINUTES.
WE'LL BE LATE.

BUT IT'S A
MAGIC ACORN! YOU
GOTTA COME SEE!

SURE, IT IS.

BABYMOUSE

THE QUEST FOR RECESS

BY JENNIFER L. HOLM & MATTHEW HOLM

CAMELOT.

THE CUPCAKE TABLE.

WHICH OF THE KNIGHTS OF THE CUPCAKE WILL ACCEPT THIS QUEST?

GULP!

I, BABYMOUSELOT, WILL FIND THE HOLY GRAIL OF RECESS!

NOBLE BABYMOUSE! BABYMOUSE!

BLINK!

BABYMOUSE!

73

MOUNT OLYMPUS.

POOF!

WHOA! WHERE AM I?

MORTAL MOUSE, YOU ARE IN THE THRONE ROOM OF THE MIGHTY ZEUS!

BLINK!

RIIINNNNGGG!!!

YOU'RE SAYING YOU'RE LATE FOR CLASS BECAUSE YOU WERE ON MOUNT OLYMPUS AND ZEUS ZAPPED YOU?

LOOK AT MY WHISKERS!

IT'S NEVER WISE TO ANGER THE GREEK GODS, BABYMOUSE.

CRACK!

HMPH.

RECESS DETENTION
• BABYMOUSE

78

WEDNESDAY.

EAT YOUR PEAS, PLEASE!

HOW'S YOUR DAY GOING, BABYMOUSE?

GREAT! ONLY TWO PERIODS UNTIL RECESS!

TODAY'S HOT LUNCH IS SPAGHETTI AND MEATBALLS.

MMM! SPAGHETTI!

NOW I JUST NEED TO WRANGLE A SEAT.

THERE WAS A NEW MOUSE AT RECESS.

RRRUUMMMBLE

AND SHE KNEW HER WAY AROUND A LASSO.

CLOP   GALLOP
CLIP

SWIRL

SWOOSH

THEY CALLED HER...

BABYMOUSE.

WHIRL

CLOP

CLIP

SWIRL

SWOOSH

TWANG!

BLINK!

TOSS!

SPLAT!

TALK ABOUT A "SPAGHETTI WESTERN."

SIGH.

WHEE!

WHEE!

THURSDAY. MATH.

MATH

$\frac{1}{2} + \frac{3}{7} =$

YOU HAVE TWENTY MINUTES TO FINISH YOUR WORK.

IN THE HISTORY OF CIVILIZATION . . .

MATH

$$\frac{1}{2} + \frac{3}{7} = y$$

$$\frac{4}{5} \times 1 = z$$

SQUINT

MATH

MARCH MARCH

$$\frac{1}{2} + \frac{3}{7} = y$$

$$\frac{4}{5} \times 1 = z$$

?

MATH WAS A NEVER-ENDING BATTLE.

BLINK!

SORRY, BABYMOUSE.

NO RECESS IF YOU DON'T FINISH YOUR CLASSWORK.

NOW WE KNOW WHY ROME FELL.

WHEE!

STUPID FRACTIONS.

RECESS DETENTION

BYMOUSE

Jiminy Sprinkles
in
"FREEZE TAG"

by Eric Wight

So much for staying away. They're coming over here!

Oh no! We're *roasted!*

What up, Cake?

H-his name is *Jiminy.*

I can take it from here, Goob—I mean, Grover.

The gang and I were wondering if you'd play Dodge Tag with us.

Sounds fun! Can my friend play, too?

Of course!

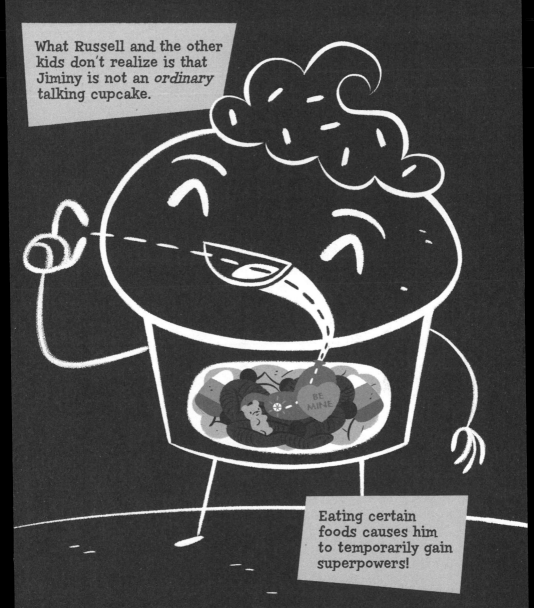

What Russell and the other kids don't realize is that Jiminy is not an *ordinary* talking cupcake.

Eating certain foods causes him to temporarily gain superpowers!

SPLOOSH!

the
end

"MY BOOK REPORT ABOUT *THE GIVING TREE*" BY JOHN HARDWICK... ONE–TWO– THREE–FOUR... TEN WORDS!

...YOU'RE NOT SERIOUS...

...HEY, ANDREW, I WAS WONDERING...

NO, YOU CAN'T COPY MY PAPER. YOU CAN LITERALLY READ IT IN TEN MINUTES AND DO IT YOURSELF.

COME ON, I WOULD DO IT FOR YOU.

THAT'S NOT THE POINT! YOU CAN'T GO THROUGH LIFE EXPECTING PEOPLE TO GIVE YOU WHATEVER YOU WANT!

THE STORY IS ABOUT A TREE... IT WAS CALLED THE GIVING TREE BECAUSE IT GAVE STUFF TO PEOPLE...THE TREE WAS BIG AND BUSHY... THIRTY–THREE, THIRTY–FOUR...

THE SCHOOL PLAY

MR. RACCOON, YOU SAVED US FROM THE WOLF! HOW CAN WE EVER REPAY YOU?

I WOULD BE HONORED IF YOU GAVE ME JUST ONE LITTLE KISS...

GURGLE

YOU PUKED ON HER.

SHE WAS TEASED FOR WEEKS AFTER THAT, EDDIE. IT WAS HORRIBLE.

BUT THAT'S WHY IT WOULD WORK! NO ONE WOULD EVER EXPECT SOPHIA WOODSMALL TO LET ME COPY HER HOMEWORK.

YOU NEVER EVEN APOLOGIZED TO HER.

...I MEANT TO... I JUST GET NERVOUS AROUND HER.

I'M GONNA GO ASK HER RIGHT NOW.

HE HAS NO SHAME. DO YOU THINK SHE'LL HELP HIM?

NO WAY. SHE WASHED HER HAIR FOR THREE HOURS THAT NIGHT.

GURGLE

UGH. HOLD IT TOGETHER, EDDIE.

HI, EDDIE!

SHHH!

HI, SOPHIA. HI, ASHA.

WHAT DO YOU WANT, PUKEBOY?

HAHAHA! THAT'S... THAT'S A GOOD ONE, ASHA!... UH, I WAS ACTUALLY JUST COMING TO SAY HI TO SOPHIA.

REALLY? BUT WE NEVER TALK TO EACH OTHER.

YEAH, WELL, I ALSO CAME TO SEE IF YOU DID THE ASSIGNMENT AND MAYBE—

DO YOU NEED TO COPY MY PAPER?

OH. EM. GEE. YOU HAVE SOME NERVE, DUDE.

HERE.

SOPHIA WOODSMALL
THE GIVING TREE

WHAT?! ARE YOU SERIOUS?!

SHE GAVE IT TO HIM!

I CAN'T LET THIS HAPPEN!

WOW! THANKS! I HONESTLY DIDN'T THINK YOU WOULD GIVE THIS TO ME!

ARE YOU OUT OF YOUR MIND?! DID YOU FORGET WHAT THIS GUY DID TO YOU?!

I THINK WE CAN ALL APPRECIATE THE IRONY OF THE SITUATION AFTER READING THE BOOK.

I'M SHOCKED.

I'M DISGUSTED.

UH, I OBVIOUSLY DIDN'T READ THE BOOK.

IN THE STORY A BOY ASKS A TREE FOR THINGS THROUGHOUT HIS ENTIRE LIFE. THE TREE AGREES TO ALL HIS REQUESTS UNTIL HE IS AN OLD MAN AND THE TREE IS JUST A STUMP WITH NOTHING MORE TO GIVE EXCEPT A PLACE TO SIT.

THE BOY WAS SO SELFISH.

I AGREE, HE DID NOTHING FOR THE TREE.

I THINK THE BOY REALLY DID CARE FOR THE TREE. IT WAS NEVER SAID OUT LOUD BUT SOMETIMES I DON'T THINK YOU HAVE TO SAY IT. MAYBE A PERSON DOESN'T HAVE THE COURAGE TO.

I FELT THERE WERE TIMES YOU WANTED TO APOLOGIZE FOR THROWING UP ON ME THAT NIGHT OF THE PLAY, BUT SOMETHING WAS HOLDING YOU BACK.

YOU'RE MY BROTHER'S BEST FRIEND SO I KNOW YOU'RE A GOOD PERSON AND DIDN'T MEAN TO DO WHAT YOU DID. THAT'S WHY I'M GIVING YOU MY HOMEWORK.

THAT AND I THINK YOU'RE ALSO KIND OF CUTE.

GROSS!

YOU COULD DO BETTER!

HEY!

BUT HE'S USING YOU! HE DIDN'T DO ANY OF THE WORK AND HE'S GETTING OFF EASY!

THE END! DONE! 300 WORDS!

I BET THAT PAPER IS AWFUL.

YOU HAVE NO IDEA.

TOUGH LOVE GOT JOHN NOWHERE. WE MIGHT BOTH GET IN TROUBLE IF YOU GET CAUGHT, BUT IN THE END YOU'RE ONLY HURTING YOURSELF BY NOT DOING YOUR OWN WORK.

RIIIIIIING

END

FOR SOPHIA AND ANDREW WOODSMALL

BABYMOUSE BINOCULARS!

TO ORDER, CALL 1-800-555-0199

ONLY THREE PAIRS LEFT!

THEY SEE EVERYTHING!

MEAN GIRLS!

STORM CLOUDS!

GRR!

CUPCAKES!

EVEN AMOEBAS!

Hey!

ORDER NOW AND GET FREE MESSY WHISKERS!

THE RAINY DAY MONITOR

STORY BY DAVE ROMAN & RAINA TELGEMEIER

ART BY RAINA TELGEMEIER · COLORS BY JOEY WEISER & MICHELE CHIDESTER

... AND SO, DUE TO THE WEATHER, TODAY'S BIG KICKBALL TOURNAMENT HAS BEEN CANCELED ...

... AND ALL RAINY DAY MONITORS WILL REPORT TO THEIR DEDICATED CLASSROOMS AT RECESS.

MR. GUFF! MR. GUFF!

WHAT IS IT, JOSH?

DO WE **HAVE** TO HAVE A RAINY DAY MONITOR?

SOMEBODY HAS TO SUPERVISE YOU GUYS DURING INDOOR RECESS.

I KNOW, BUT **OUR** RAINY DAY MONITOR IS ... IS ...

121

SIGH . . . WHAT I **REALLY** WANT TO DO IS PLAY KICKBALL.

grumble

HEY, LISTEN . . .

HAVE YOU EVER PLAYED AN RPG? LIKE DUNGEONS AND DRAGONS?

EW, NO!

THAT'S FOR NERDS!

NO, NO. LET'S HAVE YOUR KICKBALL GAME.

Rummage

WE JUST NEED SOME PAPER AND MY SPECIAL DICE.

NOW, CHOOSE YOUR TEAMS.

...

I WANT JORGE ON MY TEAM. HE'S THE BEST KICKER IN SECOND GRADE.

THAT'S WHO YOU'D CHOOSE? THIS IS **IMAGINARY**! YOU CAN CHOOSE **ANYBODY**!

ANYBODY?!

OKAY, THEN I CHOOSE...

JJ Gutierrez!
The best soccer player in the universe!

Strength +2
Dexterity +4
Charisma +6

I ALSO CHOOSE...

The President!

Charisma +8
Intelligence +9
Constitution +3

AND... Mr. Iron Ore!!

Metal +10
Mettle +3

NICE. SONIA?

OH...

Dinozilla!!

Strength +30
Intelligence -2
Fire +5

Princess Prickly Pear!

Dexterity +5
Charisma +6
Car Racing +3

Zach from One Dimension!!!

Charisma +50
Intelligence +3
Song +10

NOW . . .

I'M THE DUGOUT MASTER, SO I ROLL THE DICE. . . .

SONIA'S TEAM IS UP FIRST!

LET'S DO THIS!

PRINCESS PRICKLY PEAR IS FIRST UP. HERE COMES THE PITCH. . . .

A KICK! DOUBLE!

WOO!

ZACH KICKS, BUT THE PRESIDENT CATCHES HIS FLY BALL.

LOOK.

Shumph!

DINOZILLA DOESN'T EVEN BOTHER TO KICK—HE JUST INTIMIDATES THE OTHER TEAM WITH FIRE.

OKAY, OKAY! TWO CONSOLATION POINTS FOR SONIA'S TEAM.

JOSH'S TEAM IS UP. MR. IRON ORE TAKES THE KICKER'S PLATE.... HE KICKS...

... AND **FLIES** AROUND THE BASES! IT'S A HOME RUN!

YEAH!!!

NO FAIR!!

JJ KICKS **ANOTHER** HOME RUN!

DINOZILLA PUNTS....

DOONK!

THE PRESIDENT DIVES FOR THE BALL, AND...

...2.

2! HE MISSES!

OOF!

PRINCESS PRICKLY PEAR HOVER-JUMPS TO FIRST BASE, OUT OF MR. IRON ORE'S REACH! OOOOH!

THE VICE PRESIDENT STEPS UP TO THE PLATE.

CONCENTRATE, MR. V.P. . . .

shake shake

HE KICKS! HE MISSES! STRIKE **TWO**!

SWISH!

HERE COMES THE PITCH . . . AND THE KICK. . . .

THE END

DRAWING FUN!

Hey, Squish! Want to learn how to draw Betty in twelve easy steps?

Sounds great! I've always wanted to draw my own comics!

"Draw two circles for her glasses."

1.

Two circles...

"Next, draw her hat and her perm."

2.

Whoa! Slow down!

"Now draw her face!"

3.

What? How do I do that?

"And then the rest of her body!"

12.

What happened to step FOUR?!?!

This tutorial is terrible! Look at my drawing!

Sorry! I ran out of room. These pages are small!

★ ★ ★ ★ ABOUT THE

JENNIFER L. HOLM & MATTHEW HOLM

are the brother-sister team behind two graphic novel series, Babymouse and Squish. They grew up reading lots of comics, and they turned out just fine.

JARRETT J. KROSOCZKA

is the author and illustrator of the Lunch Lady graphic novel series, which chronicles the adventures of a spatula-wielding crime fighter. He has been reading and drawing comics since he was a kid, and he turned out all right, too.

DAV PILKEY

is the author of the phenomenally popular Captain Underpants series. He spent most of his childhood making comics very much like the one in this book. He used to get in big trouble for it at school. Now it's his job.

AUTHORS ★ ★ ★ ★

DAN SANTAT

spends most of his time writing and illustrating comics and picture books for children. When he's not doing either of those things, he is most likely playing video games or eating.

RAINA TELGEMEIER & DAVE ROMAN

are married and live under a pile of comic pages. Raina is the creator of *Smile*. Dave is the creator of the Astronaut Academy series.

URSULA VERNON

writes the comic series Dragonbreath. She still has not learned to tie her shoes correctly.

ERIC WIGHT

is the author and illustrator of the Frankie Pickle series. He ate A LOT of cupcakes to get inspiration for his new character, Jiminy Sprinkles.

GENE LUEN YANG

began drawing comics in the fifth grade. He hasn't stopped. He's a two-time National Book Award finalist and author-illustrator of the Printz Award–winning graphic novel *American Born Chinese.*